D0294630
Piglit
WOL
Pooh
This journal belongs to
eOR
Rabbit
Kanga
WOL
Pooh
Piglit
eOR
Rabbit

A. A. Milne

drawings by E. H. Shepard

Published Exclusively for W H Smith

First published in Great Britain in 1986
by Methuen Children's Books Ltd

Reprinted 1991 and 1992 exclusively in the UK
for W H Smith Limited
by Methuen Children's Books
Part of Reed International Books
Michelin House, 81 Fulham Road, London SW3 6RB

Printed and bound in Great Britain by
BPCC Hazells Ltd
Member of BPCC Ltd

INTRODUCTION

Nobody was listening, for they were all saying "Open it, Pooh," "What is it, Pooh?" "I know what it is," "No you don't" and other helpful remarks of this sort. And of course Pooh was opening it as quickly as ever he could, but without cutting the string, because you never know when a bit of string might be Useful. At last it was undone.

When Pooh saw what it was, he nearly fell down, he was so pleased. It was a Special Pencil Case. There were pencils in it marked "B" for Bear, and pencils marked "HB" for Helping Bear, and pencils marked "BB" for Brave Bear. There was a knife for sharpening the pencils, and india-rubber for rubbing out anything which you had spelt wrong, and a ruler for ruling lines for the words to walk on, and inches marked on the ruler in case you wanted to know how many inches anything was, and Blue Pencils and

Red Pencils and Green Pencils for saying special things in blue and red and green. And all these lovely things were in little pockets of their own in a Special Case which shut with a click when you clicked it. And they were all for Pooh.

Winnie-the-Pooh

This journal is all for you.

In here you can keep a diary, write your special thoughts, and record important events in your own words.

The pages include quotes and illustrations to inspire ideas.

So get out your Special Pencil Case and start writing: your favourite books, friends, things to eat (don't forget HUNNY). You can write down your feelings about things you like or don't like and dates to remember. You may even just want to draw pictures.

This is your Very Own Book to keep forever.

"But it isn't Easy," said Pooh to himself. "Because Poetry and Hums aren't things which you get, they're things which get *you*. And all you can do is to go where they can find you."

The House at Pooh Corner

"What does Christopher Robin do in the mornings? He learns. He becomes Educated. He instigorates—I *think* that is the word he mentioned, but I may be referring to something else—he instigorates Knowledge."

The House at Pooh Corner

The Old Grey Donkey, Eeyore, stood by himself in a thistly corner of the forest, his front feet well apart, his head on one side, and thought about things. Sometimes he thought sadly to himself, "Why?" and sometimes he thought, "Wherefore?"

Winnie-the-Pooh

One day, when Pooh was walking towards this bridge, he was trying to make up a piece of poetry about fir-cones, because there they were, lying about on each side of him, and he felt singy. *The House at Pooh Corner*

"Oh, Bear!" said Christopher Robin. "How I do love you!"
"So do I," said Pooh. *Winnie-the-Pooh*

Small's real name was Very Small Beetle, but he was called Small for short, when he was spoken to at all, which hardly ever happened except when somebody said: "*Really*, Small!" *The House at Pooh Corner*

The Piglet was sitting on the ground at the door of his house blowing happily at a dandelion, and wondering whether it would be this year, next year, sometime, or never. He had just discovered that it would be never, and was trying to remember what "*it*" was, and hoping it wasn't anything nice . . .

Winnie-the-Pooh

Piglet lay there, wondering what had happened. At first he thought that the whole world had blown up; and then he thought perhaps only the Forest part of it had; and then he thought that perhaps only *he* had, and he was now alone in the moon or somewhere, and would never see Christopher Robin or Pooh or Eeyore again. And then he thought, "Well, even if I'm in the moon, I needn't be face downwards all the time."

Winnie-the-Pooh

The sun was so delightfully warm, and the stone, which had been sitting in it for a long time, was so warm, too, that Pooh had almost decided to go on being Pooh in the middle of the stream for the rest of the morning. *The House at Pooh Corner*

"Piglet," said Rabbit, taking out a pencil, and licking the end of it, "you haven't any pluck."

"It is hard to be brave," said Piglet, sniffing slightly, "when you're only a Very Small Animal."

Winnie-the-Pooh

"Everybody crowds round so in this Forest. There's no Space. I never saw a more Spreading lot of animals in my life, and all in the wrong places." *The House at Pooh Corner*

Kanga and Roo were spending a quiet afternoon in a sandy part of the Forest. Baby Roo was practising very small jumps in the sand, and falling down mouse-holes and climbing out of them.

Winnie-the-Pooh

It was a warm day, and he had a long way to go. He hadn't gone more than half-way when a sort of funny feeling began to creep all over him. It began at the tip of his nose and trickled all through him and out at the soles of his feet. It was just as if somebody inside him were saying, "Now then, Pooh, time for a little something."

Winnie-the-Pooh

"*You* have a house, Piglet, and I have a house, and they are very good houses. And Christopher Robin has a house, and Owl and Kanga and Rabbit have houses, and even Rabbit's friends and relations have houses or somethings, but poor Eeyore has nothing. So what I've been thinking is: Let's build him a house." *The House at Pooh Corner*

These notices had been written by Christopher Robin, who was the only one in the forest who could spell; for Owl, wise though he was in many ways, able to read and write and spell his own name WOL, yet somehow went all to pieces over delicate words like MEASLES and BUTTERED TOAST.

Winnie-the-Pooh

It was just the day for Organizing Something, or for Writing a Notice Signed Rabbit, or for Seeing What Everybody Else Thought About It.

The House at Pooh Corner

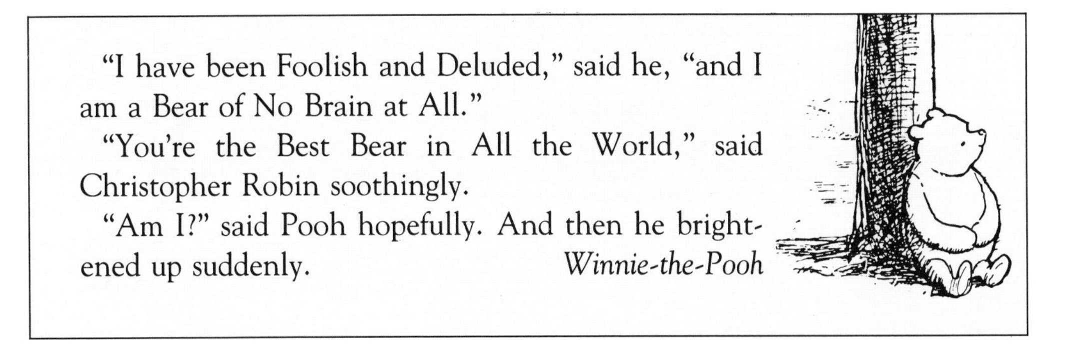

"I have been Foolish and Deluded," said he, "and I am a Bear of No Brain at All."

"You're the Best Bear in All the World," said Christopher Robin soothingly.

"Am I?" said Pooh hopefully. And then he brightened up suddenly. *Winnie-the-Pooh*

Rabbit sat down on the ground next to Pooh and, feeling much less important like that, stood up again.

The House at Pooh Corner

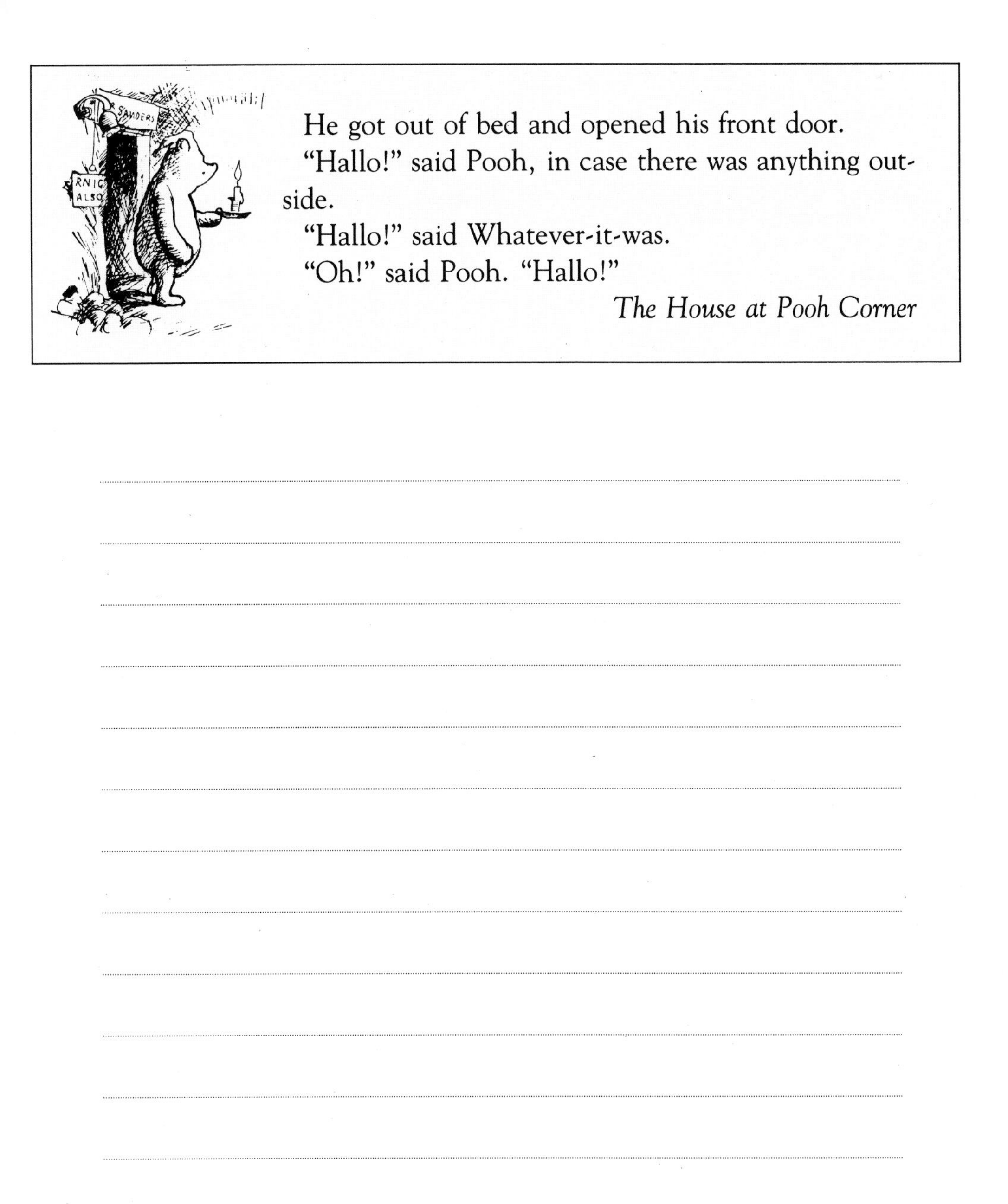

He got out of bed and opened his front door.

"Hallo!" said Pooh, in case there was anything outside.

"Hallo!" said Whatever-it-was.

"Oh!" said Pooh. "Hallo!"

The House at Pooh Corner

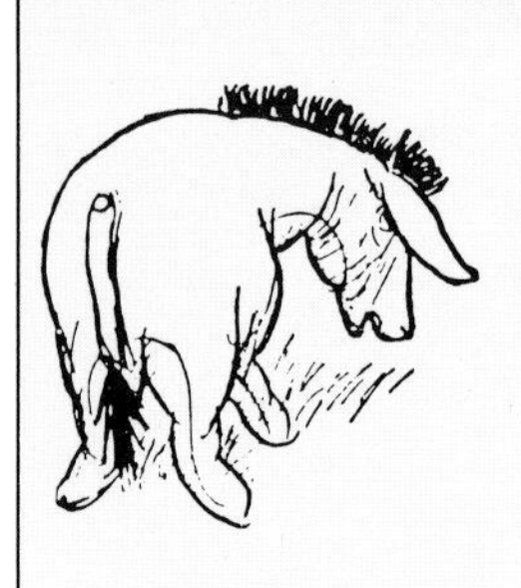

"I have just seen Eeyore," he began, "and poor Eeyore is in a Very Sad Condition, because it's his birthday, and nobody has taken any notice of it, and he's very Gloomy—you know what Eeyore is—and there he was."

Winnie-the-Pooh

"Owl," said Pooh, "I have thought of something."
"Astute and Helpful Bear," said Owl.
Pooh looked proud at being called a stout and helpful bear, and said modestly that he just happened to think of it. *The House at Pooh Corner*

Pooh thought how nice it would be if they met Christopher Robin suddenly but quite accidentally, and only because he liked Christopher Robin so much.

Winnie-the-Pooh

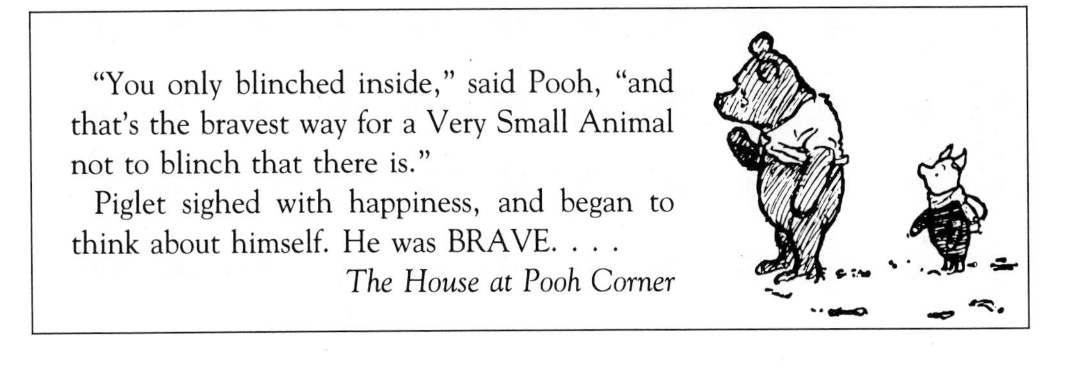

"You only blinched inside," said Pooh, "and that's the bravest way for a Very Small Animal not to blinch that there is."

Piglet sighed with happiness, and began to think about himself. He was BRAVE. . . .

The House at Pooh Corner

. . . and they all pulled together. . . .

Winnie-the-Pooh

He was humming this hum to himself, and walking along gaily, wondering what everybody else was doing, and what it felt like, being somebody else.

Winnie-the-Pooh

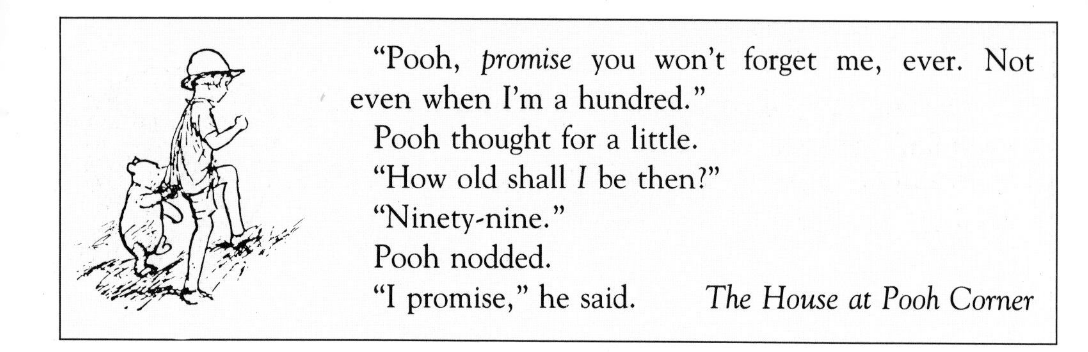

"Pooh, *promise* you won't forget me, ever. Not even when I'm a hundred."

Pooh thought for a little.

"How old shall *I* be then?"

"Ninety-nine."

Pooh nodded.

"I promise," he said. *The House at Pooh Corner*

“Eeyore,” he said solemnly, “I, Winnie-the-Pooh, will find your tail for you.”

“Thank you, Pooh,” answered Eeyore. “You’re a real friend,” said he. “Not like Some,” he said.

Winnie-the-Pooh

"Rabbit," said Pooh to himself. "I *like* talking to Rabbit. He talks about sensible things. He doesn't use long, difficult words, like Owl. He uses short, easy words, like 'What about lunch?' and 'Help yourself, Pooh.'"

The House at Pooh Corner

Piglet looked up, and looked away again. And he felt so Foolish and Uncomfortable that he almost decided to run away to Sea and be a Sailor.

The House at Pooh Corner

Roo was silent for a little while, and then he said, "Shall we eat our sandwiches, Tigger?" And Tigger said, "Yes, where are they?" And Roo said, "At the bottom of the tree." And Tigger said, "I don't think we'd better eat them just yet." So they didn't.

The House at Pooh Corner

"We can't get down, we can't get down!" cried Roo. "Isn't it fun? Pooh, isn't it fun, Tigger and I are living in a tree, like Owl, and we're going to stay here for ever and ever."

The House at Pooh Corner

"I'm afraid no meals," said Christopher Robin, "because of getting thin quicker. But we *will* read to you."

Bear began to sigh, and then found he couldn't because he was so tightly stuck; and a tear rolled down his eye, as he said:

"Then would you read a Sustaining Book, such as would help and comfort a Wedged Bear in Great Tightness?" *Winnie-the-Pooh*

"Do you know what A means little Piglet?"

"No, Eeyore, I don't."

"It means Learning, it means Education, it means all the things that you and Pooh haven't got. That's what A means."

The House at Pooh Corner

Pooh sat down on a large stone, and tried to think this out. It sounded to him like a riddle, and he was never much good at riddles, being a Bear of Very Little Brain.

Winnie-the-Pooh

"Look, Pooh!" said Piglet suddenly. "There's something in one of the Pine Trees."

"So there is!" said Pooh, looking up wonderingly. "There's an Animal."

Piglet took Pooh's arm, in case Pooh was frightened.

The House at Pooh Corner

"Hallo!" said Tigger. "I've found somebody just like me. I thought I was the only one of them."

Pooh got out of bed, and began to explain what a looking-glass was . . .

The House at Pooh Corner

"It's a Useful Pot," said Pooh. "Here it is. And it's got 'A Very Happy Birthday with love from Pooh' written on it. That's what all that writing is. And it's for putting things in. There!"

When Eeyore saw the pot, he became quite excited.

Winnie-the-Pooh

"Yes, but suppose Rabbit is out?"

"Or suppose I get stuck in his front door again, coming out, as I did once when his front door wasn't big enough?"

"Because I *know* I'm not getting fatter, but his front door may be getting thinner."

The House at Pooh Corner

And Eeyore whispered back: "I'm not saying there won't be an Accident *now*, mind you. They're funny things, Accidents. You never have them till you're having them." *The House at Pooh Corner*

"You fell on me," said Piglet, feeling himself all over.
"I didn't mean to," said Pooh sorrowfully.
"I didn't mean to be underneath," said Piglet sadly.

The House at Pooh Corner

"It's your fault, Eeyore. You've never been to see any of us. You just stay here in this one corner of the Forest waiting for the others to come to *you*. Why don't you go to *them* sometimes?"

"There may be something in what you say, Rabbit," he said at last. "I must move about more. I must come and go." *The House at Pooh Corner*

"Did you make that song up?"

"Well, I sort of made it up," said Pooh. "It isn't Brain," he went on humbly, "because You Know Why, Rabbit; but it comes to me sometimes."

The House at Pooh Corner

. . . and when the whole Escape was finished, there was Pooh sitting on his branch, dangling his legs, and there, beside him, were ten pots of honey. . . .

Winnie-the-Pooh

Kanga had felt rather motherly that morning, and Wanting to Count Things—like Roo's vests, and how many pieces of soap there were left, and the two clean spots in Tigger's feeder; so she had sent them out with a packet of watercress sandwiches for Roo and a packet of extract-of-malt sandwiches for Tigger, to have a nice long morning in the Forest not getting into mischief. And off they had gone. *The House at Pooh Corner*

Suddenly Winnie-the-Pooh stopped, and pointed excitedly in front of him. "*Look!*"

"*What?*" said Piglet, with a jump. And then to show that he hadn't been frightened, he jumped up and down once or twice in an exercising sort of way.

Winnie-the-Pooh

"What I like best in the whole world is Me and Piglet going to see You, and You saying 'What about a little something?' and Me saying, 'Well, I shouldn't mind a little something, should you, Piglet,' and it being a hummy sort of day outside, and birds singing."

The House at Pooh Corner

"Well," said Owl, "the customary procedure in such cases is as follows."

"What does Crustimoney Proseedcake mean?" said Pooh. "For I am a Bear of Very Little Brain, and long words bother me."

"It means the Thing to Do." *Winnie-the-Pooh*

"I think what I'd like best, Pooh, is I'd like you to hum it to me *now*—and—and *then* to hum it to all of us. Because then Everybody would hear it, but I could say 'Oh, yes, Pooh's told me,' and pretend not to be listening."

The House at Pooh Corner

Once upon a time, a very long time ago now, about last Friday, Winnie-the-Pooh lived in a forest all by himself under the name of Sanders.

Winnie-the-Pooh

Piglet saw what a Foolish Piglet he had been, and he was so ashamed of himself that he ran straight off home and went to bed with a headache. But Christopher Robin and Pooh went home to breakfast together.

Winnie-the-Pooh

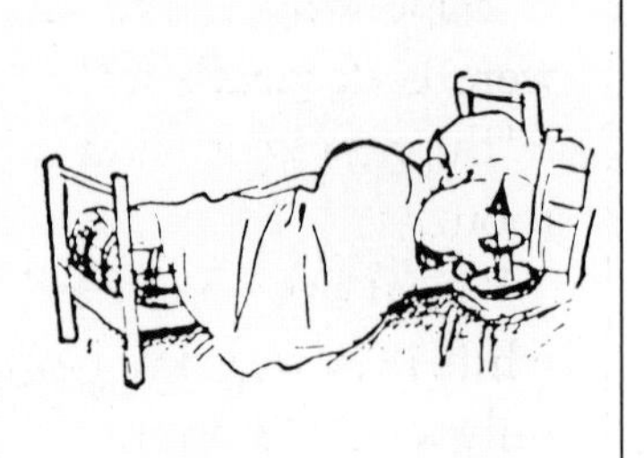

"Supposing a tree fell down, Pooh, when we were underneath it?"

"Supposing it didn't," said Pooh after careful thought.

Piglet was comforted by this, and in a little while they were knocking and ringing very cheerfully at Owl's door. *The House at Pooh Corner*

"We are all going on an Expedition," said Christopher Robin.

"Going on an Expotition?" said Pooh eagerly. "I don't think I've ever been on one of those. Where are we going to on this Expotition?"

"Expedition, silly old Bear. It's got an 'x' in it."

"Oh!" said Pooh. "I know." But he didn't really.

Winnie-the-Pooh

Piglet had got up early that morning to pick himself a bunch of violets; and when he had picked them and put them in a pot in the middle of his house, it suddenly came over him that nobody had ever picked Eeyore a bunch of violets.

The House at Pooh Corner

Christopher Robin, who was thinking of something else, said: "Where's Pooh?"—but Rabbit had gone. So he went into his house and drew a picture of Pooh going a long walk at about seven o'clock in the morning, and then he climbed to the top of his tree and climbed down again, and then he wondered what Pooh was doing and went across the Forest to see. *The House at Pooh Corner*

"Help-help and Rescue!" Piglet cried,
And showed the others where to go.
[Sing ho! for Piglet (PIGLET) ho!]
And soon the door was opened wide,
And we were both outside!
Sing ho! for Piglet, ho!
Ho!

The House at Pooh Corner

"What a long time whoever lives here is answering this door." And he knocked again.

"But Pooh," said Piglet, "it's your own house!"

"Oh!" said Pooh. "So it is," he said. "Well, let's go in."

Winnie-the-Pooh

It was a perfect morning for hurrying round to Pooh, and saying, "Very well, then, I'll tell Piglet," and then going to Piglet, and saying, "Pooh thinks—but perhaps I'd better see Owl first." It was a Captainish sort of day, when everybody said, "Yes, Rabbit" and "No, Rabbit," and waited until he had told them.

The House at Pooh Corner

"Goodbye," said Eeyore. "Mind you don't get blown away, little Piglet. You'd be missed. People would say 'Where's little Piglet been blown to?'"

The House at Pooh Corner